Doctor
Toby

written by Andrew Pattison
illustrated by Virginia Barrett

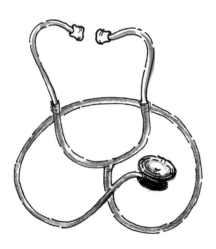

A Health Initiative
**endorsed by the
Australian Medical Association
(Victoria Branch)**

15710

published by Hyland House

This is Dr Toby. He is our family doctor. The surgery where he works is near the corner of our street.

His real name is Dr Toby Clark — but most people just call him Dr Toby. His name is written on a brass plate at the front of the surgery. His friend Dr Karen works at the surgery too.

A nice lady called Barbara helps Dr Toby. Mummy said she is the receptionist. She often talks to patients on the telephone. And she always makes sure that there are lots of books in the waiting room.

Dr Toby has known me ever since I was a baby. When I was small I sometimes cried a little when Mummy took me to see him. Now we are specially good friends. Last week he let me listen to my heart go 'lub-dup, lub-dup . . .' And one day he gave me a torch for my doctor's set.

Dr Toby has lots of interesting things in his room. He has a torch to look inside your mouth. He also has a stethoscope to listen to your chest. It always feels a bit cold on your skin.

There are jars full of cotton balls and bandages, and scales to stand on and see how much you weigh.

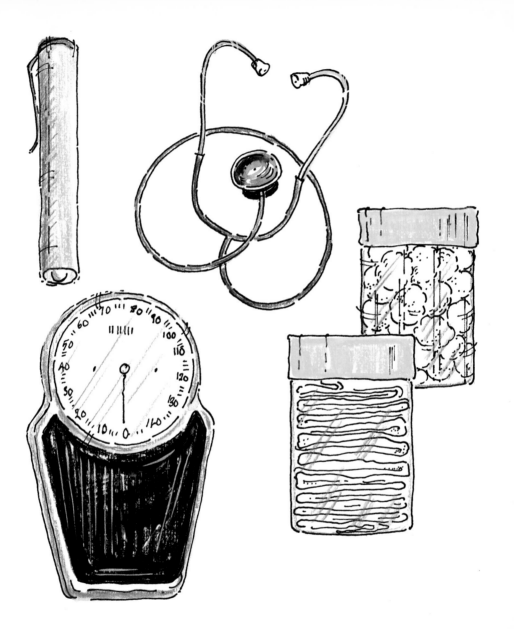

Dr Toby wears a small black thing on his waist called a pager. I once heard it go 'beep, beep, beep . . .' It printed a message on a little screen. Then Dr Toby rang the hospital to talk about a patient.

Dr Toby has children of his own too. He has lots of photos on his desk. And one day I saw him at the supermarket with his little girl . . . He was wheeling her along in the trolley.

Dr Toby can usually fix me up if I am sick. Sometimes he asks Mummy to get me some medicine from the chemist. But often he says that I will just get better by myself.

Late one night Dr Toby came to see me at our home. Mummy and Daddy had called him because I had a very bad pain in my tummy. I think Dr Toby had just got up out of bed. He wore some jeans and a fuzzy old jumper. He looked a bit different with his hair all messed up. He asked Mummy to give me some special medicine. Next day my tummy pains had all gone away.

I asked Dr Toby how he became a doctor. First he had to go to a Medical School. Then he helped in different hospitals for a few years. Now he is a family doctor with a surgery of his own.

One day my best friend Steven broke his arm. He fell off the climbing-bars at the park. Dr Toby did an X-ray to see how the arm was broken. Then he set Steven's arm in a special plaster cast. Steven let me write my name on his new plaster.

One day when my ears had been very sore Dr Toby got Mummy to take me to see another doctor called an ear specialist. That doctor looks after patients with sore ears.

Dr Toby said that there are lots of other specialist doctors — eye specialists, bone specialists, heart specialists and even specialists for your skin.

Dr Toby once went to our school to give a talk to all the children about health. He spoke about food and exercise and things we can do to keep well.

Sometimes Dr Toby goes to the hospital to see some patients there.

You don't have to be sick to be in hospital. Mummy was in hospital for a few days when my little brother was born.

I think I might be a doctor when I grow up. Maybe I could come back and help Dr Toby at his surgery.

First published in 1988 by
Hyland House Publishing Pty Limited
10 Hyland Street
South Yarra
Victoria 3141

National Library of Australia
cataloguing-in-publication data:

Pattison, Andrew.
    Dr Toby.

    ISBN 0 947062 30 0.
    ISBN 0 947062 29 7 (series).

    1. Physicians — Juvenile literature. 2. Physician
and patient — Juvenile literature. I. Barrett,
Virginia. II. Title. (Series: Pattison, Andrew.
Dr Toby books; 1).

610.69'52

Typeset by Savage Type Pty Ltd, Brisbane
Printed by Island Graphics Pty Limited